MW00994738

# Life
# ESSENTIALS

## Disciple Making Essentials Series

# Ken Adams

# Life
# ESSENTIALS

ImpactDisciples.com

# BEFORE YOU BEGIN...

Days before Jesus was crucified He prayed, *"He would bring His Father glory by completing the work He was called to do."* If we are going to be successful in fulfilling our mission in life, we need to know what our mission is. We need to have a clear sense of our mission and purpose in this life. The mission of a Christian's life comes directly from Christ! The mission of Christ's life is the mission of every Christian's life.

*Life Essentials* is a course designed to help you understand the mission and purpose of your life. As you work through these weekly lessons, remember that the truths discovered here will serve as a guide for why you exist and how to fulfill your life's mission. The biblical principles you will learn in this course will be a foundation for understanding the direction and course of your life.

In order to lay a solid foundation, I would like to recommend a few things. *First,* give your best to each lesson. Don't rush through the lessons and skim the reading. Give it your best effort and look up all the verses so that you know what God is saying. *Second,* commit yourself to the daily scripture reading. The scripture reading is designed to supplement the lesson and using the acrostic **A.C.T.S.** will help God's Word come alive to you every day. *Third,* commit yourself to the weekly memory verse. Memorizing scripture is one of the most important things you can do to grow spiritually, so give this discipline your best effort. *Fourth,* be present at the group meetings. Anyone can do the lessons on his or her own, but you can't discuss what you are learning on your own. The group time is a valuable aspect of your spiritual growth process.

Over the next few weeks, I pray that you will discover the purpose of your life, and I pray that these life essentials will be true of you for a lifetime.

Being and Building Disciples,

Ken Adams

# WEEK ONE:
# YOUR LIFE'S MISSION

**Goal:** To understand the mission for your life.

Why are you here? That is the most important question in life. Someone once said, *"The two most important days in your life are the day you were born and the day you discover why you were born."*

Understanding your life's mission or purpose is one of the most important discoveries you can have. If you do not know "why" you exist, then it is very hard to know what to do with your life. Not knowing your life's mission is like following a map without a final destination. It makes no sense!

There are lots of people, including Christians, who are struggling in life because they do not know their mission. Many people are like the man who was climbing the ladder of success only to discover it was leaning against the wrong wall! If you are spending lots of time, energy, and effort on things that do not line up with your mission, you will end up in the wrong place.

Before we go any further in discussing your life's mission, let's define it. Take a minute and write out your life's mission, as you understand it today. *My life's mission is.....*

_____
_____
_____
_____
_____
_____
_____
_____
_____
_____
_____
_____

**MEMORY VERSE**

John 17:4

**WEEKLY BIBLE READING**

Read the passage and write out an insight on at least one of the following:

**A:** Attitude to change
**C:** Command to obey
**T:** Truth to believe
**S:** Sin to confess

☐ **MONDAY**
Deuteronomy
6:1-9

# DISCOVERING YOUR MISSION

**WEEKLY BIBLE READING**

☐ **TUESDAY**
Matthew
22:23-40

Here is some great news! Discovering your life's mission is easier than you think. You don't have to read a book, listen to a bunch of CD's, or attend a seminar to discover your mission and purpose in life. You simply have to look to Jesus!

If you are a Christ follower, that means you have died to yourself and Christ lives in you. If you are dead and Christ is living in you, then that indicates that His mission is now your mission. Am I going too fast for you? When you exchanged your life for Christ's life, you took on Christ's mission. When you discover the mission of Christ's life, you have discovered the mission of every Christian's life.

The mission of Christ is incredibly clear. You can see it in two very important statements that Jesus made. We even call these statements the Great Commandment and the Great Commission. These two powerful statements define the life mission of every single Christ follower.

☐ **WEDNESDAY**
John 10:1-21

## THE GREAT COMMANDMENT: "BEING A DISCIPLE"

In Matthew chapter twenty-two, someone asked Jesus what the greatest commandment in the law was. Jesus responded in verses 37-39 with the following, *"You shall love the Lord your God with all your heart and with all your soul and with all your mind. This is the great and first commandment. And a second is like it: You shall love your neighbor as yourself."*

In this Great Commandment Jesus is clearly teaching the importance of being in right relationships with God, self, and the other people in your life. One part of why you exist is simply to be the disciple that God created you to be. Before you "do" anything for God, He simply wants you to "be" His disciple.

## THE GREAT COMMISSION: "BUILDING MORE DISCIPLES"

In Matthew chapter twenty-eight, Jesus shares with His disciples their final marching orders before leaving earth. In verses 19 and 20, Jesus commissions His disciples to, *"Go therefore and make disciples of all nations, baptizing them in the name of the Father and of the Son and of the Holy Spirit, teaching them to observe all that I have commanded you. And behold, I am with you always, to the very end of the age."*

☐ **THURSDAY**
1 John 2:1-6

In this Great Commission Jesus is clearly teaching the importance of building more disciples of Christ by going, baptizing, and teaching them to be His disciples. Another part of why you exist is to build more disciples of Christ. As you learn to "be" a disciple, you will naturally want to "build" more disciples. The doing comes out of the overflow of being.

Always remember this simple equation…
*A Great Life = A Great Commitment to the Great Commandment and the Great Commission!*

## LIVING YOUR LIFE'S MISSION

☐ **FRIDAY**
John 15:1-17

Discovering your life's mission is easy, living it is a bit more of a challenge. In other words, how do you live out the mission of being a disciple and building more disciples? How do you live in right relationships with God, yourself, and others? How do you make more disciples for Jesus? Obviously the answer to this question is a lifelong pursuit. You will spend the rest of your life seeking to live out the mission of Christ, but there are a few things you need to consider.

**You can't live what you don't know!** In order to live the mission of Jesus, you must study the life of Christ. If you want to live out what it means to be and build disciples, you need to learn from the model. What does 1 John 2:6 say? _____

_____

When you walk as Jesus walked, you are learning how to be rightly related to God, to yourself, and to the other people in your life. When you walk as Jesus walked, you are learning how to make more disciples by going, baptizing, and teaching others to obey Christ's commands.

**You can't live Christ's mission in your own power!**
In order to live the mission of Jesus, you need to let Christ live His life through you. This is what Jesus said in John 15:5. Write His words: _____

_____

_____

If Christ is not living in us, we are powerless. The Holy Spirit in you gives you the power to be a disciple and to build more disciples! Jesus empowers every believer with the supernatural ability to live in right relationships and to help teach others to do the same.

**You need others to help you live Christ's mission!**
Jesus taught His disciples to live out His mission in the context of community. He knew that we would need other believers in our lives to help us succeed in fleshing out His mission. How does Hebrews 10:24 communicate this principle? _____

_____

_____

When you are surrounded by a small group of believers, they can help you fulfill Christ's mission by praying for you, encouraging you, challenging you, and supporting you.

The next seven weeks are designed to help you discover the essentials for living out your life's mission. If you study the scriptures, seek the leading of the Holy Spirit, and do so in community, you will be well on your way to understanding your mission in a way that you may never have before.

4

# QUESTIONS FOR GROUP DISCUSSION
## OR PERSONAL REFLECTION

➤ Open your group with prayer and share a highlight from your life this past week.

➤ How much thought or energy would you say you have given to discovering your life's mission? How important is it?

➤ What did you write as your life's mission at the beginning of this lesson? Has it changed any after reading the lesson?

➤ Read Matthew 22:37-39. How does this passage help you discover part of your life's mission?

➤ How would you evaluate your life when it comes to "being" a disciple?

➤ Read Matthew 28:19-20. How does this passage help you discover part of your life's mission?

➤ How would you evaluate your life when it comes to "building" disciples?

➤ Why do we want our life's mission to be the same as Christ's life mission?

➤ How can we be sure that we are actually fleshing out the mission of Jesus in our own lives?

➤ Take a minute to share prayer concerns and pray together.

# WEEK TWO: BEING RIGHTLY RELATED TO GOD

**Goal:** Understanding what it means to be rightly related to God.

Being a disciple begins with living your life rightly related to God. Nothing else is more important to living out the right mission in life than being in a right relationship with God. If your relationship with God is not right, it will be totally impossible for you to fulfill the mission of your life! (Read that last sentence again.) When your relationship with God is right, it paves the way to make all of your other relationships better and to fulfill your mission in this life. The following diagram illustrates the way all of your relationships connect to one another.

## WHAT DOES IT MEAN TO BE RIGHTLY RELATED TO GOD?

Don't let this statement shock you. Everyone has a relationship with God. The problem is, not everyone has a "right relationship" with God.

Everyone has a relationship with God in the sense that He is the creator and they are His creation. However, sin has caused that relationship to be broken until it can be fixed.

**MEMORY VERSE**

John 10:27

**WEEKLY BIBLE READING**

Read the passage and write out an insight on at least one of the following:

**A:** Attitude to change
**C:** Command to obey
**T:** Truth to believe
**S:** Sin to confess

☐ **MONDAY**
Genesis 3:1-13

The only solution for your broken relationship with God is to be redeemed back to God through a saving relationship with Jesus Christ. Romans 5:19 says, *"For as by the one man's disobedience the many were made sinners, so by the one man's obedience the many will be made righteous."*

Jesus is the only one who can make it possible for sinners to be rightly related to God again!

Step one in being and building disciples is being rightly related to God. If a person is not living in a right relationship with God, nothing else matters!

When a person is rightly related to God, it can change every other relationship in life. A right relationship with God can change how you relate to you. A right relationship with God can change the way you relate to family members. A right relationship with God can change your relationships with members of your spiritual family. A right relationship with God can change how you relate to your human family. In summary, being rightly related to God changes how you relate to the entire world! This is why Jesus said, *"Go make disciples of all nations!"*

Helping people become rightly related to the God who created them is the answer to all of the world's problems. This is why the first and foremost priority of being and building disciples is helping people "be rightly related to God."

God wants us to **be** something before he ever expects us to **do** something! Being rightly related to Him is where disciple making begins.

## RELATIONSHIP AND FELLOWSHIP

Being rightly related to God means having a restored relationship with God and continual fellowship with God. Until a person is forgiven of their sin and restored to a right relationship with God, they can never "be" who they were created to be. Once a person has been forgiven and saved by God's grace, the goal is to live in fellowship with God.

**A restored relationship:** What does the Bible say about our spiritual condition according to Romans 3:23?

_____

_____

❏ **THURSDAY**
2 Corinthians
2:1-17

This verse clearly teaches that a person is born with a broken relationship with God and not a right relationship with God. What did Christ do for us while we were in this broken state according to Romans 5:8? _____

_____

_____

John 3:16 echoes what Paul said in Romans 5:8. What did Jesus do according to that verse? _____

_____

_____

What should a person do in order to restore their relationship with God based on Romans 10:9? _____

_____

_____

❏ **FRIDAY**
Matthew
25:14-30

The bad news is that everyone enters life with a broken relationship with God. The good news is that through faith in Jesus forgiveness can be granted and that relationship restored. Has your relationship with God been restored through Christ?

_____

_____

_____

**Ongoing fellowship:** God desires for everyone to have a relationship with Him, but He also desires that everyone experience continual fellowship with Him. Fellowship is that sense of nearness and closeness that comes from seeking God and connecting with him. What

_____

_____

_____

_____

_____

_____

_____

_____

_____

_____

_____

_____

_____

_____

_____

_____

_____

_____

_____

_____

This "drawing near" that James is speaking about is the kind of close fellowship we can experience with God. Like a sheep and a shepherd, a Christian can know God and experience His presence in his or her life. What does John 10:27 say?_____

In the book of Exodus we see an example of a fellowship relationship in the life of Moses. In Exodus 33:7-11 where would Moses go and meet with God? ___

How is Moses' experience with God described in verse 11? _____

We might not hear God's voice in an audible way, but we can still know His presence and know Him in a personal way. That is fellowship!

## THE FELLOWSHIP RELATIONSHIP

It is important to remember that being in a right relationship with God means having both a relationship and fellowship at the same time. Here is an example that might help you understand it better. My father and I will always have a relationship. The moment I was born, I became his son and he was my father. Nothing can ever change the fact that we are related. However, we may be living in a broken relationship that needs restoring. With forgiveness and healing our relationship can be renewed and rebuilt. That restored relationship gives us the opportunity to cultivate fellowship with each other. If we connect with each other and communicate with each other, our restored relationship will become a close fellowship.

In the same way that a father and son experience a fellowship relationship, God wants to experience that fellowship relationship with you. God has a relationship with you as your creator, but that relationship is broken until Christ restores you with forgiveness and grace. Once your relationship with God is restored and you are saved, you can begin to experience deeper fellowship with God. You can know God in a very personal and spiritual way.

Two of the most important questions you must ask are: do you have a right relationship with God and are you experiencing continual fellowship with God?

## QUESTIONS FOR GROUP DISCUSSION
## OR PERSONAL REFLECTION

➤ Open your group with prayer and share a praise for something that happened in the past week.

➤ Why does having a right relationship with God mean so much to your life?

➤ What kinds of things keep us from having a right relationship with God?

➤ Explain the difference between a relationship and fellowship.

➤ When and how did you enter into a right relationship with God?

➤ How would you describe your current state of fellowship with God?

➤ Read John 10:27. What kinds of things help you stay close to God?

➤ Can a person have a relationship with God without fellowship?

➤ Take a minute and share prayer concerns and pray together.

# WEEK THREE: BEING RIGHTLY RELATED TO YOU

**Goal:** Understanding how to be rightly related to you.

Being a disciple begins with being rightly related to God and then being rightly related to oneself. In fact, a person cannot truly be rightly related to himself or herself until they are rightly related to God. You will never know your mission and purpose in life until you are right with yourself. So many people struggle with their purpose and mission because they make the mistake of thinking "they" are their purpose and mission. News flash: you are not your mission!

Discovering that you are not the mission will put you well on your way to truly discovering your mission and purpose in this life. Your mission is to love God and love others, not to love you.

## WHAT DOES IT MEAN TO BE RIGHTLY RELATED TO SELF?

Everyone agrees that we need a right relationship with ourself, but not everyone agrees on how it happens.

In fact, the world says the secret to being rightly related to self is through self-esteem, self-worth, and self-image. The Bible says, *"He must increase, but I must decrease."* (John 3:30)

## WEEKLY BIBLE READING

Read the passage and write out an insight on at least one of the following:

**A:** Attitude to change
**C:** Command to obey
**T:** Truth to believe
**S:** Sin to confess

☐ **MONDAY**
Romans 8:1-11

Being in a right relationship with self will never come from within you; it comes from above you! It is ""Christ in you" that gives meaning to life. Without Christ, life means nothing.

Once you are rightly related to God, then you can become rightly related to you. Until your relationship with God gets right, your relationship with you will always be wrong!

When you begin to see yourself as "in Christ," everything about the way you relate to you changes. Your worth is found in who you are in Christ. Your esteem is not limited to how you see you, but rather how God sees you. Your image is being transformed into the image of Christ.

In a nutshell, the best way to be rightly related to you is to do away with you! Paul said it like this in Galatians 2:20, *"I have been crucified with Christ. It is no longer I who live, but Christ who lives in me. And the life I now live in the flesh I live by faith in the Son of God, who loved me and gave himself for me."*

As you begin to live a crucified life, you will discover how it helps you relate better to others. When you have died to yourself, you will find it much easier to be rightly related to the people around you.

The story is told of a missionary who was headed into a tribe of savages. Someone said, "You will not come back; you will die." The missionary responded, "I am already dead!"

This missionary had discovered the key to living in right relationships. He was rightly related to himself and others because he was allowing Christ to live through him. The best way to be rightly related to you is to have less of you and more of Him!

# THE CRUCIFIED LIFE

The world's way of being rightly related to you and God's way of you being rightly related to you are completely opposite. The world says that in order to be rightly related to you, you must find yourself. God says the way to be rightly related to you is to lose self. The key to being rightly related to you is to die to self and be alive "in Christ."

☐ **THURSDAY**
Ephesians
2:1-10

In order to better understand how to be rightly related to self, let's take a minute and define self correctly. Your identity is defined in four ways.

*Who you are!*

*What you do!*

*How you think!*

*Whose you are!*

If someone asked you to describe yourself, you would most likely use one or all of the statements above to describe your identity. When you have died to self and are alive in Christ, these four statements take on brand new meaning. Let's take a look at what they mean.

☐ **FRIDAY**
Colossians
3:1-17

**Who you are!** When someone describes "who you are," they are identifying you according to your attributes. Attributes are the characteristics that people use to identify you. They may use words like, "nice, kind, patience, caring, or loving." On the other hand, they may use words like, "mean, impatient, hateful, insensitive, or resentful." The difference between those two descriptions is directly related to your relationship with Christ. How does Galatians 5:22, 23 describe the person who is walking in the Spirit? _____

_____

_____

**What you do!** When someone describes "what you do," they are describing you according to your actions. Actions are behaviors that people can use to identify you. If your actions are self-controlled, people may say that you, "steal, cheat, or lie." On the other hand, if your actions are Spirit-controlled, people may say that you, "give, serve, or share." The words used to describe the way you act are determined by who is in control of your life. What does 1 Peter 1:16 say? _____

_____

_____

_____

**How you think!** When someone describes "how you think," they are describing you according to your attitude. Attitude is a mindset that can be used to describe your identity. If people say you are "negative, critical, or pessimistic," then you do not have a Christ-like attitude. On the other hand, if people describe your attitude as "positive, optimistic, and encouraging," you are thinking with the mind of Christ. What does Philippians 2:5 say?

_____

_____

_____

**Whose you are!** When someone describes "whose you are," they are describing you according to who you are controlled by. What does 2 Corinthians 5:17 say about the Christian? _____

_____

_____

_____

When you die to self and let Christ live in you, it makes you a new creation. "In Christ" your attributes are new, your actions are new, and your attitude is new. The old has passed away and the new is come!

Being rightly related to yourself can only happen when you decrease and Christ increases. When you place your life on the altar as a living sacrifice, the Lord can make you the person you were created to be. When your attributes, actions, and attitudes have been placed on the altar, that opens the door for Christ to live His attributes, actions, and attitudes through you. This is the key to the crucified life.

## QUESTIONS FOR GROUP DISCUSSION OR PERSONAL REFLECTION

➤ Open your group with prayer and share a high or a low from your past week.

➤ Give some examples of what it looks like when people are <u>not</u> rightly related to themselves.

➤ What does it look like when people are living in a right relationship to themselves?

➤ How does being rightly related to God impact your relationship with yourself?

➤ Read Galatians 2:20 and explain what it means to be "crucified with Christ."

➤ Read Romans 6:6. How is your relationship with you impacted by whether you are self-controlled or spirit-controlled?

➤ When you are decreasing and Christ is increasing, how are your attributes, actions, and attitudes different?

➤ How can your relationship with yourself affect the way you relate to other people?

➤ Take a minute and share prayer concerns and pray for each other.

# WEEK FOUR: BEING RIGHTLY RELATED TO OTHERS

**Goal:** Understanding how to be rightly related to other people.

Being a disciple begins by being rightly related to God. It then moves to being rightly related to self, and finally it moves to being rightly related to others. Until you are rightly related to God and to yourself, you cannot truly be rightly related to the world around you. Here's an example of how this happens. If you are battling with insecurity, it will affect the way you relate to other people. Insecurity is a result of not knowing who you are "in Christ." This is just one of many examples of how all of life's relationships are connected. The following diagram shows how all of life's relationships build off your relationship with God.

## WHAT DOES IT MEAN TO BE RIGHTLY RELATED TO OTHERS?

After thirty years of ministry, I have concluded that one of the biggest problems people have today is learning to live in right "relationships." In fact, some of the wealthiest people I know are miserable because they are living in broken relationships, and some of the poorest

## MEMORY VERSE

John 15:12

## WEEKLY BIBLE READING

Read the passage and write out an insight on at least one of the following:

**A:** Attitude to change
**C:** Command to obey
**T:** Truth to believe
**S:** Sin to confess

☐ **MONDAY**
Luke 10:29-37

people I know are the happiest because they are living in right relationships. I say this simply to illustrate how important it is to live in right relationships with the significant people in your life.

Being a disciple of Jesus means learning to live in right relationships. This begins with your relationship with God. Your relationship with God impacts your relationship with you, and that impacts your relationship with others. I can assure you that if you are not right with God, you will not be rightly related to others. As Christ changes you and makes you into the person He created you to be, it will make all of your other relationships in life better! This is why we are called to "make disciples"!

Making disciples is the best way to build better marriages, better families, better churches, better businesses, better communities, better nations, and a better world.

When a person becomes more like Jesus in their character and conduct, they will always relate better to the people around them. The best way to change the world is to change the way people relate to people, and the best way to do that is to teach them to live like Jesus!

In John 15:12 Jesus said, *"This is my commandment, that you love one another as I have loved you."* When we learn to love like Jesus loved, we will begin to live in right relationships.

Loving like Jesus loved will change the way you relate to everyone in your life. Christ's love is patient and it is kind. It does not envy, it does not boast, it is not proud. It is not rude, it is not self-seeking, it is not easily angered, and it keeps no record of wrongs. Love does not delight in evil but rejoices with the truth. Christ's love always protects, always trusts, always hopes, and it always perseveres. Christ's love never fails!

# PRIORITIES AND PRINCIPLES

The relationships you have with people in your life are built on one of two different things. They are either built on "circumstances and feelings" or "priorities and principles." The difference is that circumstances and feelings change. They come and go, and they are like building a relationship on sinking sand. On the other hand priorities and principles seldom if ever change. They are much more stable and steady, and building a relationship on priorities and principles is like building on a rock. The following diagram is a great picture of what building a relationship on priorities and principles looks like.

❏ **THURSDAY**
Luke 6:27-36

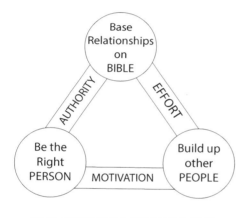

# RELATIONAL PRIORITIES

❏ **FRIDAY**
Proverbs 16:1-33

There are three timeless priorities that can guide and strengthen every relationship in your life if you live by them.

**Base all relationships on biblical truth!** The Bible has the answer to every relationship issue you will ever face. The Bible speaks about communication, conflict resolution, sexuality, money, child rearing, and unrealistic expectations. The Bible is the ultimate relationship handbook, but you have to read it!

**Be the right person!** The second relational priority to build on is simply being the person you are supposed to be. You can be the husband, father, friend, and neigh-

21

bor you are supposed to be when you allow the Holy Spirit to transform you into Christ's image.

**Build up other people!** The third priority needed to build a strong relationship is the priority of building up others. When you are looking for ways to build up others and give to them, you will be amazed at how this impacts a relationship. Learn to see yourself as a resource rather than a recipient and you might be surprised how good your relationships can be.

## RELATIONAL PRINCIPLES

The relational priorities that you need to improve your relational world must be driven by three essential principles.

**Upward authority!** The Bible has all the relational truth you will ever need! The question is: will you submit to it? I've talked to countless people who know what the Bible says about their relational conflicts, but they are simply not willing to obey what God says.

**Inward motivation!** Being the right person cannot happen unless an individual is motivated to change and be transformed. When two people are motivated to be the right person, it is amazing how much better relationships work.

**Outward energy!** It takes energy to build up other people. You have to work at encouraging and serving the other people in your life. If you will focus on building up other people and looking for ways to encourage them and support them, you will be shocked at how much better your relationships will be.

## QUESTIONS FOR GROUP DISCUSSION
## OR PERSONAL REFLECTION

➤ Open your group with prayer and share a high or low from your past week.

➤ How important do you think relationships are to most of the people you know?

➤ What do you feel are some of the greatest attacks against all relationships in life?

➤ Read Romans 12:18. What does this verse teach you about relationships? Is there a relationship where you need to apply this truth today?

➤ Read James 4:11. How do your words impact relational harmony in your life? Is there a relationship where you are tearing down more than building up?

➤ Read Ephesians 4:32. How can this priority of biblical truth make a difference in a relational stalemate?

➤ What things does God need to change in you that would have an immediate effect on your closest relationships?

➤ Which relationship in your life right now do you most need God to work?

➤ Take a minute to share prayer concerns and pray together.

# WEEK FIVE: BUILDING MORE DISCIPLES BY GOING

**Goal:** Understanding how to make disciples "as you go."

As you begin to develop in the process of learning how to live in right relationships, you can begin to build more disciples as well. You do not have to completely "arrive" before you can start making more disciples. The truth is you will never "arrive," so you can start being part of the process of making disciples the minute you receive Christ. In fact, being in the process of reaching people and making disciples will even aid your growth as a disciple. So we could say that seeking to build more disciples helps you to become a disciple, and as you become a disciple, it will cause you to want to build more disciples.

It is important to realize that part of your mission in life is to help build more disciples of Christ. Some people live their entire lives and never make one single disciple. Don't be one of those people! God has made you a disciple so that you could in turn make more disciples. The following diagram will help you see how to build more disciples.

## MEMORY VERSE

Romans 10:14

## WEEKLY BIBLE READING

Read the passage and write out an insight on at least one of the following:

**A:** Attitude to change
**C:** Command to obey
**T:** Truth to believe
**S:** Sin to confess

☐ **MONDAY**
John 4:1-26

# WHAT DOES IT MEAN TO BUILD DISCIPLES BY GOING?

When Jesus gave His final commission to His disciples to *"make disciples,"* He started it with the word, *"GO"*!

The process of helping disconnected people become disciples has always been a commitment to go and reach people who are far from God. Jesus modeled this commitment himself when He left the comfort of heaven and came to this earth to *"seek and save"* that which was lost. (Luke 19:10)

When Jesus used the word "go" in the original language, it was actually used as a participle, which literally meant, *"As you go, make disciples."* In this context the command would literally mean as you go to work, as you go to school, as you go shopping, as you go to the gym, or as you go home.

Jesus is indicating that the Great Commission is actually more of a lifestyle than an event. In other words, making disciples by going is something we do everywhere we go!

"Going" is the first step in the process of making disciples. As Paul says in Romans 10:14, *"How then will they call on him in whom they have not believed? And how are they to believe in him of whom they have never heard? And how are they to hear without someone preaching?"*

The movement of making disciples that Jesus started two thousand years ago is a movement of messengers. We must take the message of salvation to those who have not heard it. To those who are disconnected!

How would you evaluate the step of "going" in your life these days? Are more people hearing because you are sharing? Are more disconnected people getting connected to Christ because you are taking the message to people far from God?

❐ **THURSDAY**
Acts 5:27:42

It will be impossible to build more disciples unless you are willing to do so *"as you go."* If you open up your eyes to the people around you, you might be surprised at how many more disciples you will be able to build.

Living a life of helping disconnected people become disciples is exactly what Jesus did, and it is the very life He wants us to live.

## SEEK AND SAVE

Jesus made it crystal clear that one of the reasons He was here on this planet was to *"seek and to save the lost."* With this part of Christ's life mission being extremely clear, is there any wonder why it wouldn't be just as clear that this is part of the mission of every disciple? Anyone who is following Jesus ought to have the same mission He had. This includes "seeking and saving" that which is lost.

❐ **FRIDAY**
Romans 15:8-33

In order to live out the mission of seeking and saving that which is lost, there are four things which should be understood in the disciple.

**A clear mission!** What did Jesus clearly tell His disciples to do Mark 16:15? _____

How does this verse relate to what Jesus said in Acts 1:8? _____
_____
_____

It appears that Jesus made the mission of going to "all nations" very clear. We build more disciples as we go and share the "good news." Someone has said, "The main thing is to keep the main thing the main thing." I believe they were talking about evangelism. We cannot make disciples if we are not sharing Christ "as we go." If the eternal destiny of each person really matters, then how can "sharing" Christ not be the main thing?

**The proper motive!** Jesus made it incredibly clear that there is only one reason why we need to share His message. He states this reason in John 3:16. What is it? _

God's love for the world is the only motivation we need for sharing the message of Christ "as we go." If we love the way Jesus loved, then we will want to share the news of salvation with everyone who needs to hear it. If we have the love of God in our hearts, we would not want one single person to miss out on knowing Christ. What did Jesus say in Matthew 9:12?

**The correct methodology!** Jesus modeled for His disciples exactly how He wanted them to make disciples. Everywhere Jesus went, He demonstrated the "as you go" lifestyle. Jesus continually connected with people, He prayed for people, He looked for people who were open to His message, and He built bridges to help people connect to God. In Luke 19:1-10 we see the methodology of Jesus on display. Who did Jesus connect with in this text?

How was it a relational connection? _____

_____

_____

How did Jesus build a bridge for Zacchaeus to cross over? _____

_____

_____

Jesus was clearly connecting with Zacchaeus as "he was going" from one place to the next.

**The right message!** Jesus was the "living word," but He also communicated very clearly the message of salvation. In John chapter 3 we see Jesus communicating the message of salvation to a man named Nicodemus. Jesus clearly communicated our **need**. What is it according to John 3:3?_____

_____

_____

Jesus clearly communicated God's **provision**. What can God provide according to John 3:6?_____

_____

_____

Finally, Jesus clearly communicated our **decision**. What must we do to be born again according to John 3:15? _____

_____

_____

Communicating the right message always includes communicating our need for salvation, God's provision for salvation, and our decision to trust and believe for salvation.

## QUESTIONS FOR GROUP DISCUSSION OR PERSONAL REFLECTION

➤ Open your group with prayer and share something God has been teaching you recently.

➤ Read Matthew 28:19, 20 and explain the three steps in making disciples.

➤ How does the idea of making disciples "as you go" differ from other ideas on making disciples?

➤ Read Luke 19:10. In what ways did Christ's life match up with this statement?

➤ How would you say your life matches up with Luke 19:10?

➤ What places are you consistently going where you could be making disciples?

➤ Read Luke 19:1-10. What lessons can we learn from this passage about the way we should reach out to lost people?

➤ Who is the Zacchaeus in your life today?

➤ Take a minute and pray for the person or people in your life that need to hear the message of Jesus.

# WEEK SIX: BUILDING MORE DISCIPLES BY BAPTIZING

**Goal:** Understanding how to make disciples by baptizing them.

If I told you that part of your mission in life is to baptize people, you might not buy it. In fact, I am guessing you probably have not baptized many people, if any at all. But it is very clear in Matthew 28:19 that Jesus told His disciples to "go and make disciples of all nations, baptizing them." Since Jesus made it clear that we are to baptize people in order to make disciples, maybe that command includes more than just the act of being baptized in water. Maybe Jesus is talking about the fact that being baptized in water represents a connection to Him and His church. Water baptism is actually just the symbol of a commitment to identify with Christ and His Church. I believe this tells us that our mission in life is to help as many people as possible come to "identify" with Christ and His church, and being baptized is part of that commitment.

**MEMORY VERSE**

Acts 2:41

**WEEKLY BIBLE READING**

Read the passage and write out an insight on at least one of the following:

**A:** Attitude to change
**C:** Command to obey
**T:** Truth to believe
**S:** Sin to confess

☐ **MONDAY**
Matthew 3:11-17

# WHAT DOES IT MEAN TO BUILD DISCIPLES BY BAPTIZING?

Jesus was very clear that one part of the disciple-making strategy was to include the act of baptism. The directive is clear, but let's think about the reasons behind it. Why did Jesus want baptism to be an integral part of disciple making?

The most important reason Jesus had for making disciples by baptizing was that it identified people with Him. When a person was immersed in water, it was an act of identifying with Christ's death, burial, and resurrection. When a person was baptized, it was a very public event. Once baptized, a person would be known as a Christ follower by all their friends, family, and even their enemies.

A second reason that baptism was an important part of the disciple-making strategy was that it identified Christ followers with each other. The public act of baptism was a symbol of belonging to a faith community. When a person was baptized, it meant they belonged to God's spiritual family. Many times this meant their own biological family would have nothing more to do with them.

You can see now why baptism was such an important part of Christ's disciple-making strategy. It truly was an act of identification, and symbolized a connection with both Christ and His followers. In Jesus' day you would not take the step of baptism unless you were really serious about your commitment to follow Him. Baptism meant you were a committed disciple of Jesus Christ!

Baptism in today's world should mean the same thing that it did in Christ's world. It should be the symbol that shows the world your identification with Christ and His followers. It is an outward sign of an inward commitment. A committed Christ follower should never be ashamed of going public with their faith through baptism.

If you are serious about making disciples, you must be committed to helping people take the step of baptism and identifying with a spiritual family. Be committed to helping people understand how important it is to be baptized and how pleased God is when we take this important step of obedience. What did God say when Jesus was baptized according to Matthew 3:17? _____

☐ **THURSDAY**
Ephesians
4:1-16

_____

_____

## BELIEVING AND BELONGING

When a person in first century Jerusalem went through the waters of baptism, it communicated two very important things for all who witnessed it. First, it meant that the person being baptized was identifying with Jesus Christ. It indicated a new set of beliefs. Secondly, it meant that the person being baptized was identifying with a new group of people. It indicated they belonged to the community of Christ followers.

In today's world baptism should mean the same thing it did in the first century. Baptism should mean believing and belonging. Baptism is really an outward expression of an inward commitment. Baptism was the time when a person would go public with their faith and identify with Christ and His church.

☐ **FRIDAY**
Colossians 3:12-17

## HELPING PEOPLE IDENTIFY

If the process of making disciples can be broken down into *going, baptizing,* and *teaching,* then the second step in the process, the baptizing or going public part, can be considered "identifying." Like a wedding ring outwardly identifies an inward commitment between two people, baptism outwardly identifies an inward commitment between a person and God. When you help people take the step of baptism, you are helping them "identify" with Christ and His church.

_____

_____

_____

_____

_____

_____

_____

_____

_____

_____

_____

_____

_____

_____

_____

_____

_____

_____

_____

**Baptism identifies you as a believer in Christ!**
What happened in Jerusalem according to Acts 2:41?___
_____
_____

In Acts chapter two, three thousand people believed in what Christ had done for them, and they placed their faith in Him. After placing their faith in Christ, they were outwardly baptized as a sign of identification with Christ.

**Baptism identifies you as a member of Christ's Church!** In Acts 2:42 how are those who had been baptized as believers described? _____
_____
_____

In Jerusalem those who had identified themselves as believers in Christ also identified themselves with the community of believers known as the church. Once a believer identified with the community of believers, they got involved in that community. They were involved in worship in the temple and meeting with other believers in their houses.

Identifying with Christ and His church is every bit as important today as it was for the first church. Everyone that commits to being a disciple of Jesus should take the step of baptism as an act of obedience to Jesus. This outward act of professing your faith in Christ and commitment to His church is a sign that will let everyone where you stand. What did Jesus say in Matthew 10:32, 33? _____
_____
_____

If you are really looking to find your mission in life, then you must look no further than Jesus' words. Your mission is to make disciples as you go and to help them identify with Christ and His church through believing and belonging. Public baptism is the outward sign that indicates this step of obedience has been taken. Don't go through the rest of your life missing the opportunity to help as many people identify with Christ and His church as you possibly can.

## QUESTIONS FOR GROUP DISCUSSION
## OR PERSONAL REFLECTION

➤ Open your group with prayer and share a person you have reached out to recently.

➤ Read Acts 2:41. What do you think baptism meant to Christians in the early church? In what ways has it changed or remained the same?

➤ Why do you think Christ chose water baptism as the symbol for identifying with Him and His church?

➤ What are some things that keep people from taking the step of baptism today?

➤ How would baptism be different for a person converting from Islam versus a person who was raised in America?

➤ Why is the practice of baptism by immersion so important?

➤ Describe your baptism experience. What did it mean to you?

➤ How does baptism and church membership connect to one another?

➤ Why is church membership important? Are you a committed member of a local church?

➤ Take a minute and share your prayer concerns and pray together.

# WEEK SEVEN: BUILDING MORE DISCIPLES BY TEACHING

**Goal:** Understanding how to make disciples by teaching them.

One of the reasons you exist is to make more disciples, and one of the ways you do that is by teaching someone else how to be one. If the teachings and life of Jesus illustrate anything, they clearly illustrate that our life's mission is to teach people how to be disciples of Christ. However, there are very few Christians that ever teach someone else how to be a disciple of Christ. You cannot fully accomplish your life's mission if you do not understand how to make a disciple by teaching. It seems like the enemy has been very successful in keeping believers from really understanding this mission. To prove my point, how many disciples have you taught? _____

**MEMORY VERSE**

2 Timothy 2:2

**WEEKLY BIBLE READING**

Read the passage and write out an insight on at least one of the following:

**A:** Attitude to change
**C:** Command to obey
**T:** Truth to believe
**S:** Sin to confess

☐ **MONDAY**
Matthew 28:18-20

# WHAT DOES IT MEAN TO BUILD DISCIPLES BY TEACHING?

Jesus told His disciples to make more disciples by *"teaching them to observe all that I have commanded you."* It is clear that the disciple-making process includes teaching and training. Once an individual has identified with Christ through baptism, the goal is to teach and train them how to be a disciple and build more disciples.

Sadly, most churches stop the disciple-making process at *"baptizing."* Some churches do the going and baptizing parts, but they stop short of the teaching part. This is like having a birth without having any growth. We have churches today that are full of Christians wearing spiritual diapers when they ought to be mature disciples!

The imperative Christ gave His disciples was to *"[teach] them to observe all that [he] commanded."* The commandments Jesus had given were to love the Lord your God with all your heart, soul, and mind, and to love your neighbor as yourself. When you love God and others, it will motivate you to be a disciple of Christ and to help others to become disciples of Christ.

The mission of every Christian and every church is to help people come to *know* Christ, to *grow* in Christ, and then to *go* for Christ. This is the only way we can *"make disciples of all nations."*

Jesus spent three years training His disciples for their mission. He taught them His character and His conduct, and then He sent them out to do the same. Jesus wanted His disciples to be like Him and to do what He did. He even sent His Spirit to empower them to live the life He wanted them to live and to fulfill the mission He had given them to accomplish.

Disciple making still requires the component of teaching. We need Christians and churches that are effectively making disciples not just busy with activities. A person can be active and not productive! The mission to make disciples of all nations demands that we *go, baptize,* and *teach*!

## TEACHING DISCIPLES

☐ **THURSDAY**
Philippians
2:19-30

Jesus was very intentional about the way He taught His disciples. He had a plan. In just a short period of years, Jesus took His disciples from being unschooled and ordinary men to becoming world changers. This did not happen by accident. Jesus used four criteria for teaching His disciples while living together in a small group community. These same elements incorporated in a small group are the keys to teaching disciples to this day. Let's look closer at these four elements.

☐ **FRIDAY**
2 Timothy
1:3-14

**Content:** One quick read through the Gospels and you will conclude that Jesus used content or information to teach His disciples. Jesus taught His disciples "truth" in a large group setting, small group setting, and in a one-on-one setting. What was Jesus doing in Mark 6:2?_____

_____

Who was with Jesus in Mark 6:1? _____

_____

Jesus did not answer every Bible question the disciples had, but He did give them enough information to accomplish His mission. How are you receiving content in your life right now?

_____

_____

**Contact:** Sometimes when a person reads the biblical accounts of Jesus, he or she overlooks all the time Jesus spent making contact with His disciples. Jesus used the relational time He spent with His disciples to teach them how to live and lead. What does Mark 3:14 say about Jesus and His disciples? _____

_____

_____

Read Mark 6:30-31 and explain how this illustrates the "with Him" approach that Jesus used. _____

_____

_____

**Context:** Jesus taught His disciples by giving them firsthand ministry experiences. In other words, Jesus took those He was teaching with Him while doing ministry. Jesus did not keep His disciples in the lecture hall. He took them into the laboratory of ministry. Who is Jesus spending time with in Matthew 9:10? _____

_____

_____

Who is with Jesus while He is connecting with the tax collectors and sinners? _____

_____

Jesus did a tremendous amount of teaching while His disciples went along with Him in ministry situations. Can you give an example of a time you went with someone in a ministry situation or took someone with you? _____

_____

_____

**Correction:** Jesus not only taught His disciples with content, contact, and context, He also taught them through correction. What did Jesus say to His disciples in Matthew 8:26? _____

_____

_____

What happened in Matthew 19:13-14? _____

_____

_____

What was taking place in Matthew 20:20-24? _____

_____

_____

Over and over again, Jesus had to correct His disciples. They lacked faith, they misunderstood Jesus' actions, and they argued with each other. Jesus knew His disciples had to learn, and correction was a part of the process. Have you ever had someone bring correction to your spiritual growth process? _____

_____

_____

## QUESTIONS FOR GROUP DISCUSSION
## OR PERSONAL REFLECTION

➤ Open your group with prayer and share how you have been doing in your walk with God this past week.

➤ Explain how you have personally walked through the steps of becoming a disciple. (Going, baptizing, teaching)

➤ Read Mark 1:22. How does the element of teaching look different today than it did with Jesus and His disciples?

➤ Read Mark 2:23. What does this verse tell you about the way Jesus used "contact" in teaching His disciples?

➤ What are some ways disciples can be taught through "contact" in our day and time?

➤ Read Mark 6:7. How does this passage illustrate the use of "context" in disciple making?

➤ In what ways can "context" be used to make disciples in this small group?

➤ Read 2 Timothy 3:16. What types of things is Scripture good for?

➤ How did Jesus use "correction" in teaching His disciples? How do most people view correction today?

➤ Take a minute to share prayer concerns and pray together.

# A FEW FINAL THOUGHTS...

Congratulations! You have finished *Life Essentials*. Hopefully you have applied yourself wholeheartedly to this study and are growing as a disciple of Christ.

Now that you know the mission and purpose of your life, I hope that you will be successful in being and doing what Christ put you here to do. If you continue to apply these traits and live by these truths, you will grow closer to God, become more like Christ, and find your place in His church.

It is time now to take your next step as a disciple and work through another course in the Disciple Making Essentials Series. You may also want to check out more resources from Impact Ministries. Check out the Impact Ministries page in the back of this booklet or look us up on the web at impactdisciples.com.

## KEEP LIVING CHRIST'S MISSION!

 Inspiring People and Churches to Be and Build Disciples of Jesus Christ

# EXPLORE

We invite you to EXPLORE and DISCOVER the concepts of DISCIPLE MAKING by checking out the following RESOURCES.

◆The Impact Blog ◆The Impact Newsletter
◆The Impact Audio and Video Podcasts

# EDUCATE

We encourage you to LEARN more about DISCIPLE MAKING through our written RESOURCES and TRAINING opportunities.

◆The DMC Training ◆315 Leadership Training ◆Free Resources

# ESTABLISH

We seek to HELP you start a DISCIPLE MAKING MOVE-MENT by showing you how to LAUNCH a disciple making

◆The Impact Weekend ◆The Essentials ◆Vision Consultation

# ENGAGE

We invite you to JOIN with Impact Ministries in spreading the VISION of DISCIPLE MAKING around the WORLD through several involvement opportunities.

◆Join our Prayer Team ◆Be an Impact Trainer ◆Partner with Us

# CONTACT US

◆ImpactDisciples.com ◆Info@ImpactDisciples.com ◆678.854.9322

73892223R00029

Made in the USA
Columbia, SC
23 July 2017